Contents

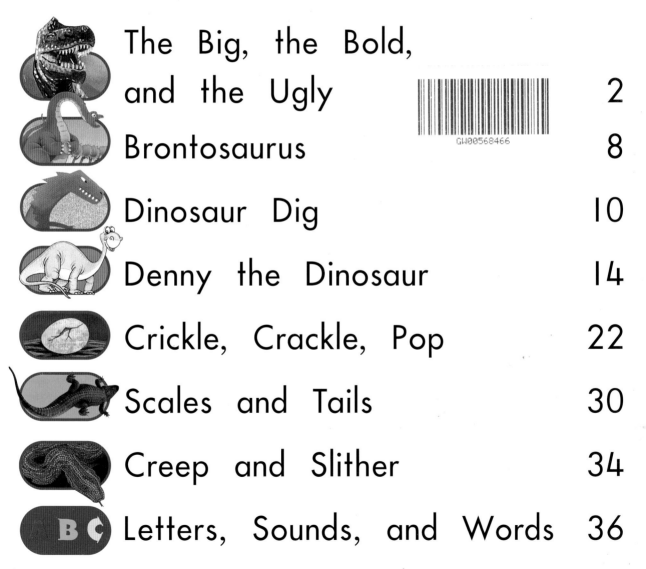

GW00568466

The Big, the Bold, and the Ugly

Written by Ian Douglas • Illustrated by Leonardo Meschini

Some dinosaurs were **big**.
They were as big as a truck.
They ate plants.
Their *long* necks
helped them get their food.

Some dinosaurs were **bold**. They were predators (pred-a-tors). Their *sharp* teeth and *sharp* claws helped them get their food.

4

Some dinosaurs were **ugly**. They had horns and spikes to keep them safe.

Some dinosaurs were *fast*. They could run away from predators.

Make a
Dinosaur
Fridge Magnet

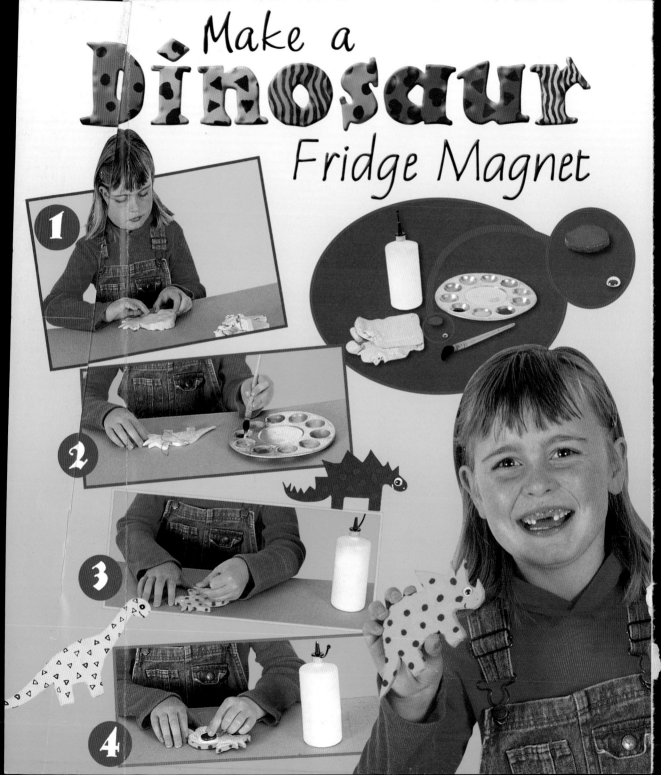

1

2

3

4

Dinosaur Dig

Some scientists study dinosaurs.
They look for fossils.
They look for bones.
They put the bones
together to make
skeletons of dinosaurs.

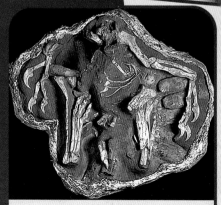

Fossils

Dinosaurs
laid eggs.
Some dinosaurs made nests
for their eggs.
Some dinosaurs looked after
their eggs and babies.

Denny the DINOSAUR

Written by Richard Gunther · Illustrated by Kelvin Hawley

One day, I found a big egg.

It went **crickle, crackle, POP**

and out came a little dinosaur.

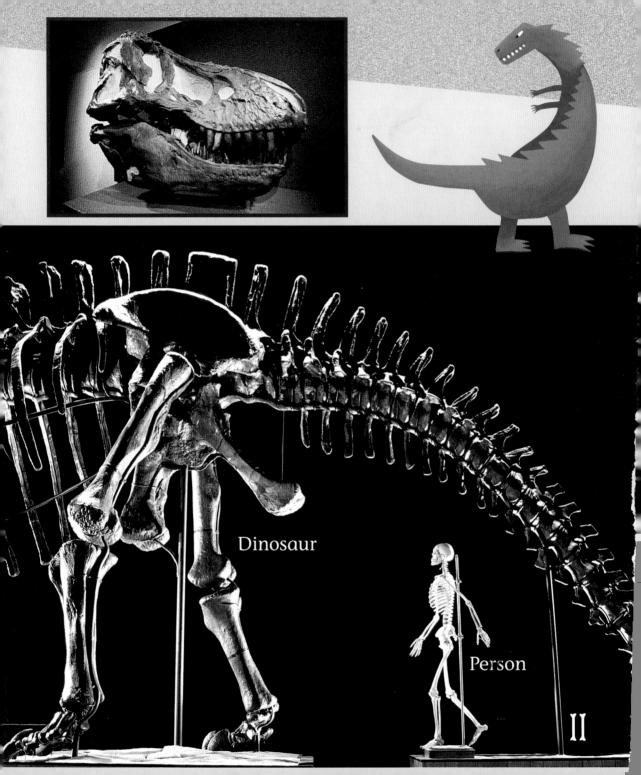

Dinosaur

Person

II

Dinosaur
Crossword Puzzle

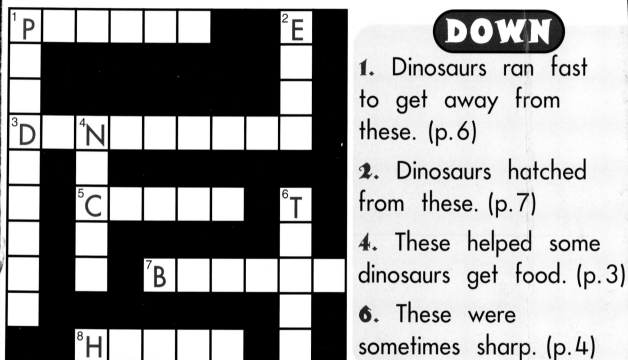

DOWN

1. Dinosaurs ran fast to get away from these. (p.6)

2. Dinosaurs hatched from these. (p.7)

4. These helped some dinosaurs get food. (p.3)

6. These were sometimes sharp. (p.4)

ACROSS

1. Some dinosaurs ate these. (p.3)
3. Some of these were as big as a truck. (p.3)
5. These helped some dinosaurs get food. (p.4)
7. Some dinosaurs looked after these. (p.7)
8. Some dinosaurs had these to keep them safe. (p.5)

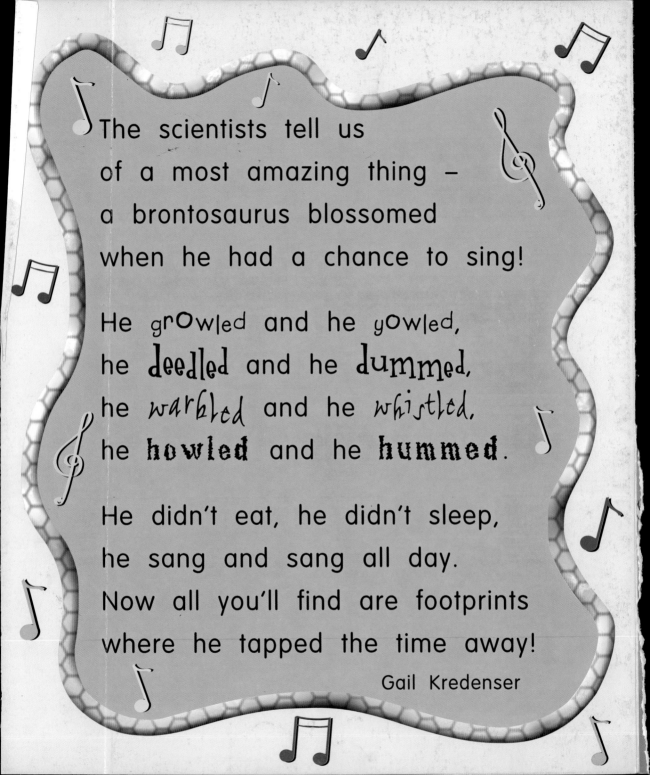

The scientists tell us
of a most amazing thing –
a brontosaurus blossomed
when he had a chance to sing!

He growled and he yowled,
he deedled and he dummed,
he warbled and he whistled,
he howled and he hummed.

He didn't eat, he didn't sleep,
he sang and sang all day.
Now all you'll find are footprints
where he tapped the time away!

Gail Kredenser

"Denny the dinosaur is too big
to live here with us," said Dad.
"He will have to go!"

"But Denny the dinosaur
is my pet," I said.
"Please can he stay here with us?
I'll get him a job.
Please don't make him go!"

Denny and I looked for jobs.
We looked for jobs in shops.
We looked for jobs in schools.

We looked
and we looked
and we looked.

19

Then, at last, we found a job!
It was a good job for a dinosaur.

Now Denny goes
to work every day.
He is happy.

And I am happy, too.
I still have my pet dinosaur.

CRICKLE, CRACKLE, POP

Written by Debra Holt Williams • Illustrated by Meng-Feng Wu

"Come and look," called Deer.
"There's an egg over here."

"Come and look," called Porcupine.
"There's an egg over here."

The animals looked at the egg.
"Whose egg is it?" they asked.
"We'll look after it."

Then a big snake came along.
It curled up around the egg.

"Go away!" shouted Deer.

"Go away!" shouted Porcupine.
"Go away from that egg."

But the big snake
did not go away. 69

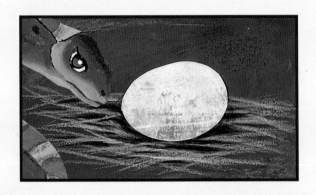

24

25

Then...

crickle,

crackle,

POP!

The egg cracked open.

Out came a little snake.

"It's Snake's egg!"

shouted the animals.

27

"We are so sorry we shouted at you," said the animals.

"Don't be s-s-silly," said Snake.
"You were trying to s-s-save my egg.
And s-s-so was I."

Then Snake and Baby Snake s-s-slid away into the forest.

28

29

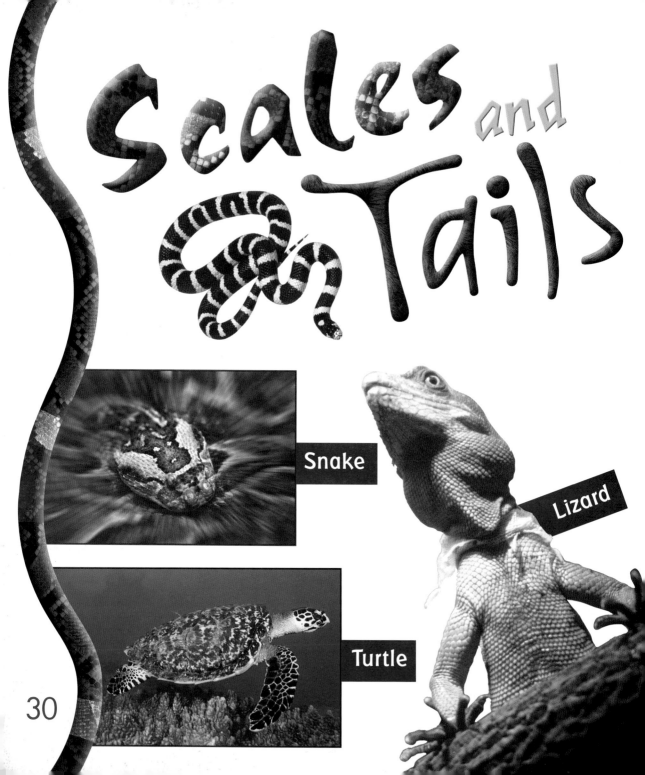

Scales and Tails

Snake

Lizard

Turtle

Lizard

Snake

Snakes are reptiles.
Crocodiles and lizards
and turtles are reptiles, too.

Turtle

Crocodile

All reptiles are
cold-blooded.
They have scaly skin.

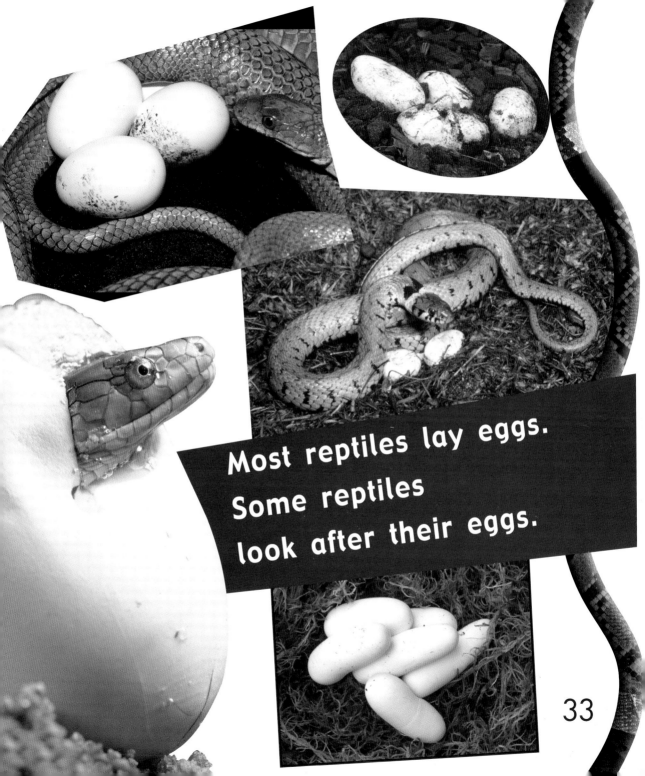

Most reptiles lay eggs.
Some reptiles
look after their eggs.

33

Creep and Slither

Slip, slide,
snake is hungry,
quick, hide.

Tongue flicks out,
smells a frog,
snake slides quietly
to the log.

Tongue flicks out,
open wide,
goodbye frog,
too late to hide.

Creep, slither,
slide along,
tummy full,
frog is gone.

Words I Know

as	called	some	these
away	little	their	they
big	please	them	were
bigger	shouted	there's	with

Sounds I Know

-ake snake

-ide hide, slide

Letters That Go Together

cr  sl  sn